D1459766

Tell Your Life Story

The Write Your Own Autobiography Guided Journal

Jeffrey Mason

Hear Your Story Book

"The two most important days in your life are the day you are born and the day you find out why."
– Mark Twain

This Is the
Life Story of

_____

"The purpose of life is to live it, to taste experience to the utmost, to reach out eagerly and without fear for newer and richer experience."
– Eleanor Roosevelt

TABLE OF CONTENTS

"BABIES ARE SUCH A NICE WAY TO START PEOPLE."   6

CHILDHOOD   16

MY TEENAGE YEARS   28

ENTERING ADULTHOOD   42

"LIFE CAN ONLY BE UNDERSTOOD BACKWARDS; BUT IT MUST BE LIVED FORWARDS."   52

LIFE'S LEARNINGS   58

MY FAMILY WHEN I WAS GROWING UP   62

MY PARENTS   68

MY GRANDPARENTS   82

MY SIBLINGS   88

"LOVE DOESN'T MAKE THE WORLD GO 'ROUND. LOVE IS WHAT MAKES THE RIDE WORTHWHILE."   96

BECOMING A PARENT   104

MILESTONE MOMENTS   121

"ONE CANNOT THINK WELL, LOVE WELL, SLEEP WELL, IF ONE HAS NOT DINED WELL."   129

ALL THE LITTLE THINGS THAT MAKE ME, ME   137

I AM GRATEFULL FOR   149

MY LIFE'S JOURNEY   159

FORGIVENESS AND MOVING FORWARD   166

THE MUSIC, BOOKS, MOVIES, AND SHOWS OF MY LIFE   173

MY WISHES   183

LETTERS AND MEMORIES   193

"Babies are such a nice way to start people." – Don Herold

"Diaper backward spells repaid."
– Marshall McLuhan

My birthdate is...

_____

The town I was born in was...

_____

And the place I was born was (hospital, at home, side of the road)...

_____

My full name at birth was...

_____

_____

This name was selected because...

_____

_____

_____

If they had given me a vote, I would have asked them to name me...

_____

_____

_____

"A toddler can do more in one unsupervised moment than most people can do all day." – Author Unknown

The name I prefer people call me now is...

_____

_____

_____

I weighed this much when I was born...

_____

And I was this long...

_____

My parents were this age when they had me...

_____

_____

My first words were...

_____

_____

I took my first steps at age...

_____

_____

"A baby is God's opinion that the world should go on!"
– Carl Sandburg

The stories I have been told about the day I was born are...

_____

_____

_____

_____

_____

_____

_____

_____

_____

_____

_____

_____

"I was chosen, I was wanted, I was loved, I was the missing piece, I was adopted." – Author Unknown

If you were adopted...

I was this age when my parents adopted me...

_____

When I was this age, I found out that I had been adopted...

_____

I was told by...

_____

_____

The story of me being told about my adoption is...

_____

_____

_____

_____

_____

_____

_____

"We didn't give you the gift of life. Life gave us the gift of you." – Author Unknown

This is what I know about my birth parents...

_____

_____

_____

_____

_____

_____

After all these years, I still have these questions about my birth parents and me being adopted...

_____

_____

_____

_____

_____

_____

"Every baby born into the world is a finer one than the last." – Charles Dickens

When my parents talk about how I was as a baby, they describe me this way...

_____

_____

_____

_____

_____

_____

_____

_____

_____

_____

_____

_____

"A baby is a blank check made payable to the human race." – Barbara Christine Seifert

According to those who know, I really loved these songs when I was a baby...

_____

_____

_____

_____

And these toys...

_____

_____

_____

And these books...

_____

_____

_____

And this is where I slept...

_____

_____

What happened the year I was born?

(Google the following for the year you were born.)

Notable and historical events that occurred the year I was born...

_____

_____

_____

_____

_____

The movie that won the Academy Award for Best Picture...

_____

A few popular movies that came out the year I was born...

_____

_____

_____

_____

What happened the year I was born?

A few songs that were on the top of the music charts...

_____

_____

_____

_____

Famous people who were born the same month and year I was...

_____

_____

_____

_____

The prices of the following items were...

- A loaf of bread: _____

- A gallon of milk: _____

- A cup of coffee: _____

- The average cost of a new home: _____

- A first-class stamp: _____

- A gallon of gas: _____

- A movie ticket: _____

"Children see magic because they believe in magic."
– Author Unknown

"Childhood is like being drunk; everyone remembers what you did, except you." – Author Unknown

When I was a kid, most people called me…

_____

But sometimes they would use this nickname…

_____

I was given that nickname because…

_____

_____

I would describe myself when I was a kid this way…

_____

_____

_____

_____

…and my childhood this way…

_____

_____

_____

_____

When I was a kid, I remember...

When I was a kid, I remember playing these games...

_____

_____

_____

_____

And cherishing these toys...

_____

_____

_____

_____

And loving these television shows...

_____

_____

_____

_____

When I was a kid, I remember...

And these movies...

_____

_____

_____

_____

_____

And these songs...

_____

_____

_____

_____

And these books...

_____

_____

_____

_____

"Sometimes my childhood memories sneak out of my eyes and roll down my cheeks. – Author Unknown

During my elementary school years, my best friends were...

_____

_____

_____

_____

The last time I communicated with them was...

_____

_____

_____

The elementary school teacher that I most fondly remember is...

_____

_____

The thing I most remember about them is...

_____

_____

_____

"Kids: they dance before they learn there is anything that isn't music." – William Stafford

My regular chores included...

_____

_____

_____

_____

In return for doing these tasks, I received an allowance of...

_____

_____

When I had money, I would typically spend it on...

_____

_____

_____

When I was a kid, I dreamed of becoming a...

_____

_____

_____

"At some point in your childhood, you and your friends went outside to play together for the last time, and nobody knew it." – Author Unknown

Of all the pets we had, the ones I most fondly remember are...

_____

_____

_____

_____

_____

If I could be a kid again for just one day, I would...

_____

_____

_____

_____

_____

_____

"Some days I wish I could go back to my childhood. Not to change anything, but to feel a few things twice." – Author Unknown

One of my most favorite childhood memories is...

_____

_____

_____

_____

_____

_____

_____

_____

_____

_____

_____

_____

"You know children are growing up when they start asking questions that have answers."
– John J. Plomp

Focusing on this memory and other positive memories from my childhood makes me feel this way about my life then and my life now...

_____

_____

_____

_____

_____

_____

_____

_____

_____

_____

_____

"Childhood is a chance for kids to discover who they are before the world tells them who they should be."
– Author Unknown

This is where we lived during my elementary and junior high school years...

_____

_____

_____

I would describe where we lived this way...

_____

_____

_____

_____

_____

During the years of my childhood, I spent my summers doing...

_____

_____

_____

My childhood bedroom looked like this...

If I had to describe it, I would say the overall theme was...

_____

_____

The walls were this color...

_____

My bedding looked like this...

_____

_____

I had these things on the walls...

_____

_____

_____

Additional important details include...

_____

_____

_____

_____

_____

"If you carry your childhood with you, you never become older." – Abraham Sutzkever

It is common for kids to have an attachment to an object such as a specific blanket or toy or stuffed animal. For me, that item was...

_____

_____

_____

The name I had for this item was...

_____

The story of how this special item came into my life is...

_____

_____

_____

When I close my eyes and think about this important part of me and my childhood, I feel...

_____

_____

_____

_____

"Teenager: when you are too young to do half the things you want to do and too old for the other half."
– Author Unknown

"High School: the mouse race to prepare you for the rat race." – Author Unknown

I would describe myself when I was a teenager this way...

_____

_____

_____

_____

During my teenage years, I participated in this coming-of-age tradition (confirmation, bat mitzvah, bar mitzvah, other)...

_____

_____

_____

This is how I dressed and styled my hair in my high school years...

_____

_____

_____

_____

When I was a teenager...

I loved these bands/musicians...

_____

_____

_____

_____

And these songs...

_____

_____

_____

And these movies...

_____

_____

_____

_____

When I was a teenager...

And these television shows...

_____

_____

_____

_____

_____

And these books...

_____

_____

_____

_____

And doing these activities...

_____

_____

_____

_____

"Having a teenager can cause parents to wonder about each other's heredity."
– Author Unknown

During my teenage years, the people I mainly hung out with were...

_____

_____

_____

_____

_____

The last time we talked was...

_____

_____

_____

My parents' opinion of my choice in friends was...

_____

_____

_____

_____

_____

"Teenagehood – that time in life when you show your individuality by looking like everyone else."
– Author Unknown

A typical weekend night during my high school years was spent...

_____

_____

_____

_____

_____

My curfew in high school was...

_____

_____

One memorable time I missed my curfew was because I was...

_____

_____

_____

_____

"If you want to recapture your youth, cut off their allowance." – Al Bernstein

My parents' response to me missing my curfew was...

_____

_____

_____

_____

I would describe my high school dating life this way...

_____

_____

_____

I got my license when I was this old...

_____

To get my license, I had to take my driving test this many times...

_____

The principal person who taught me how to drive was...

_____

_____

"Education is what remains after one has forgotten what one has learned in school." – Albert Einstein

The car I learned to drive in was a (year, make, and model)...

_____

I got my first car when I was this age...

_____

My first car was a (year, make, and model)...

_____

The year I graduated from high school was...

_____

My graduating class had this many students in it...

_____

My grades were typically in this range...

_____

_____

My favorite and least favorite subjects were...

_____

_____

_____

"In school, you're taught a lesson and then given a test.
In life, you're given a test that teaches you a lesson."
– Tom Bodett

The school activities and sports that I participated in were...

_____

_____

_____

_____

_____

_____

The things I liked about high school were...

_____

_____

_____

_____

_____

_____

"The scariest part of raising a teenager is remembering the things you did when you were a teenager."
– Author Unknown

...and these are the things I disliked...

_____

_____

_____

_____

When I was a teenager, I spent my summers...

_____

_____

_____

_____

_____

_____

_____

"Home is the nicest word there is."
– Laura Ingalls Wilder

During my high school years, we lived here...

_____

_____

_____

_____

I would describe where we lived this way...

_____

_____

_____

_____

_____

_____

_____

My bedroom from my teenage years looked like this...

If I had to describe it, I would say the overall theme was...

_____

_____

The walls were this color...

_____

My bedding looked like this...

_____

_____

I had these things on the walls...

_____

_____

And my favorite place to hide things was...

_____

Additional important details include...

_____

_____

_____

_____

"I don't trust anybody who looks back on the years from 14 to 18 with any enjoyment." – Stephen King

Knowing what I know now, the advice I would give my teenage self is...

_____

_____

_____

_____

_____

_____

_____

_____

_____

_____

_____

_____

"Experience is a good school. But the fees are high."
– Heinrich Heine

A teacher, coach, or mentor that had a huge impact on me becoming who I am today is...

_____

_____

_____

The specific influences they had on me and my life were...

_____

_____

_____

_____

_____

_____

_____

_____

_____

"Adulthood is like a dog going to the vet; we're all excited for the car ride until we realize where we're actually going." – Author Unknown

"Growing up is losing some illusions, in order to acquire others." – Virginia Woolf

After high school I made the choice to...

☐ Start college.

☐ Join the military.

☐ Get a job.

☐ Take a break.

☐ Other: _____

I made this decision because...

_____

_____

_____

_____

_____

_____

Looking back, this is how I now feel about my decision...

☐ It was the right one, at the right time.

☐ It was the right direction to go in, but the wrong time to do it.

☐ You can't get them all right.

☐ The jury's still out.

"Becoming an adult is like looking both ways before you cross the street and then getting hit by an airplane." – Author Unknown

I think that this was the correct or incorrect decision because...

_____

_____

_____

_____

_____

_____

This period impacted my life in this way...

_____

_____

_____

_____

_____

"So much of being an adult is pretending you know what you're doing and then Googling for an answer."
– Author Unknown

If I had a redo, I would make these changes to this period of my life...

_____

_____

_____

_____

_____

_____

I got my first job when I was this age...

_____

The job was...

_____

_____

...and I was paid this much...

_____

"That alarming moment when you look for an adult and realize that you *are an adult*. So, you look for an adultier adult." – Author Unknown

So far, the total number of jobs I have had in my lifetime is...

_____

The first job I ever quit was...

_____

And I have been fired from this many jobs...

_____

A few of my favorite jobs were...

_____

_____

_____

_____

...and my least favorites...

_____

_____

_____

_____

"Some day you will be old enough to start reading fairy tales again."
– C.S. Lewis

The best boss I've ever had was...

_____

_____

_____

The reason they were such a great manager was...

_____

_____

_____

_____

_____

_____

_____

_____

"Common sense is the collection of prejudices acquired by age eighteen." – Albert Einstein

The worst boss I've ever had was...

_____

_____

The reason they were such a lousy manager was...

_____

_____

_____

_____

_____

_____

_____

_____

_____

"It does not matter how slowly you go as long as you do not stop." – Confucius

These are the places where I have lived during my life; I have included when and why I moved to each one...

_____

_____

_____

_____

_____

_____

_____

_____

_____

_____

My first apartment in six questions...

The first place I lived where I paid for it on my own was...

_____

_____

_____

This is how old I was when I moved there...

_____

This place had this many bedrooms and bathrooms...

_____

_____

I lived there with...

_____

_____

_____

_____

My share of the rent/mortgage was...

_____

_____

My first apartment in six questions...

This is how I would describe this place...

_____

_____

_____

_____

_____

_____

_____

_____

_____

_____

_____

_____

"Life can only be understood backwards; but it must be lived forwards." – Soren Kierkegaard

"To find yourself, think for yourself."
– Socrates

If I were to write an autobiography, the title would be...

_____

_____

_____

One of my favorite quotes is...

_____

_____

_____

The central values I have tried to live my life by are...

_____

_____

_____

_____

_____

"The only journey is the journey within."
– Rainer Maria Rilke

I am who I am today in large part because of these experiences...

_____

_____

_____

_____

_____

_____

_____

_____

_____

_____

_____

_____

_____

"Those who wish to sing, always find a song."
– Swedish Proverb

And these people...

_____

_____

_____

_____

_____

_____

_____

_____

_____

_____

_____

_____

"It takes courage to grow up and become who you really are." – ee cummings

A few of my proudest personal accomplishments are...

_____

_____

_____

_____

_____

_____

_____

_____

_____

_____

_____

_____

"The more you know yourself, the more patience you have for what you see in others." – Erik Erikson

The hardest thing I have had to overcome in my life is...

_____

_____

_____

_____

I succeeded in overcoming this challenge because of these decisions, actions, and people...

_____

_____

_____

_____

_____

"A little learning is a dangerous thing." – Alexander Pope

I was this age when I learned to...

- Say my A, B, C's: _____

- Read: _____

- Write my name: _____

- Write my name in cursive: _____

- Tie my shoes: _____

- Get dressed by myself: _____

- Do laundry: _____

- Iron: _____

- Sew a button on: _____

- Take public transportation: _____

- Roller skate: _____

- Skateboard: _____

- Ride a bike (two-wheel): _____

- Ride a horse: _____

- Ride a motorcycle: _____

- Drive a car: _____

- Parallel park: _____

- Drive a stick shift car: _____

- Put gas in a car: _____

- Change a flat tire: _____

- Change a car's oil: _____

I was this age when I learned to...

- Do a cartwheel: _____

- Swim: _____

- Dive from a diving board: _____

- Catch a ball: _____

- Throw a ball: _____

- Slow dance: _____

- Fast dance: _____

- Whistle: _____

- Play a musical instrument: _____

- Grocery shop on my own: _____

- Make a cup of coffee: _____

- Open a bottle of wine (corked): _____

- Make a cocktail: _____

- Cook a meal: _____

- Set the table: _____

- Host a party: _____

- Do dishes: _____

- Read a map: _____

- Tell time: _____

- Wake up by using an alarm: _____

- Write a check: _____

I was this age when I learned to...

- Take care of a pet: _____

- Hold a baby: _____

- Change a diaper: _____

- Calm a crying baby: _____

- Feed a baby: _____

- Do addition and subtraction: _____

- Do multiplication and division: _____

- Do my taxes: _____

- Properly kiss: _____

- Appreciate what "the birds and the bees" really means: _____

- Shuffle cards: _____

- Play poker: _____

- Play pool: _____

- Vacuum: _____

- Mow a yard: _____

- Use a screwdriver: _____

- Use a saw: _____

- Change a lightbulb: _____

- Unclog a toilet: _____

- Hang a picture: _____

- Shave: _____

"Family: where life begins and love never ends." – Author Unknown

"Home isn't a place. Home is people."
– Author Unknown

The television family that reminds me the most of my family when I was growing up is...

_____

_____

_____

We ate dinner together this number of times each week...

_____

_____

When we did eat together, the meal typically followed this routine...

_____

_____

_____

_____

_____

The person who usually cooked was...

_____

_____

"In time of test, family is best."
– Burmese Proverb

And the clean up afterwards was usually done by...

_____

_____

A few of my favorite things we would eat for dinner included...

_____

_____

_____

_____

_____

The holiday that was the biggest deal in our family was...

_____

_____

_____

_____

"Family: 1. a group of people who know and love you the most; 2. and drive you nuts." – Author Unknown

We would celebrate this holiday by...

_____

_____

_____

_____

_____

_____

_____

_____

_____

_____

_____

"A happy family is but an earlier heaven."
– George Bernard Shaw

When it comes to religion in my family when I was growing up:

☐ Religion was a big part of my growing up years.

☐ We were religious, but only occasionally attended formal services.

☐ We had our own traditions.

☐ Religion wasn't a part of my early years.

☐ Other: _____

_____

_____

The way that my family's religious traditions and beliefs impacted my current views and religious traditions is...

_____

_____

_____

_____

_____

_____

_____

Our extended family in ten questions...

The kindest person in our extended family is...

_____

The smartest is...

_____

The most athletic is...

_____

The most artistic...

_____

The funniest...

_____

The calmest...

_____

The most generous...

_____

The best cook...

_____

The handiest...

_____

The person who holds the entire extended family together is...

_____

"Parent: an example of a word that is a noun before you are one and a verb after you are."

– Author Unknown

"If at first you don't succeed, try doing it the way mom told you to in the beginning." – Author Unknown

My mother's full name is...

_____

...and her maiden name is...

_____

This is where she was born...

_____

...and where she grew up...

_____

Her family was from this/these part(s) of the world...

_____

_____

Her highest level of schooling was...

_____

_____

And her occupations have been...

_____

_____

_____

"Life began with waking up and loving my mother's face." – George Eliot

The way I would describe my mother is...

_____

_____

_____

_____

_____

_____

_____

_____

She was good at many things, but was especially talented and skilled at...

_____

_____

_____

_____

"My mom used to tell us, 'I will always love you; I just don't like you right now.'" – Pam Mason

My mom and I are alike in these ways...

_____

_____

_____

_____

_____

And this is how we are different...

_____

_____

_____

_____

_____

"Sometimes I open my mouth and my mother comes out." – Bridgette Canton

I would describe our relationship when I was a kid this way...

_____

_____

_____

_____

...and this way during my teens...

_____

_____

_____

_____

...and in my later years...

_____

_____

_____

_____

"All that I am, or hope to be, I owe to my angel mother." – Abraham Lincoln

One of my favorite memories of my mother is...

_____

_____

_____

_____

_____

_____

Some of the best advice she gave me was...

_____

_____

_____

_____

_____

"I believe that what we become depends on what our fathers teach us at odd moments, when they aren't trying to teach us." – Umberto Eco

My father's full name is...

_____

His mother's maiden name was...

_____

This is where he was born...

_____

...and where he grew up...

_____

His family was from this/these part(s) of the world...

_____

_____

His highest level of schooling was...

_____

_____

His occupations have been...

_____

_____

_____

"One father is more than a hundred schoolmasters." – George Herbert

The way I would describe my father is...

_____

_____

_____

_____

_____

_____

_____

_____

He was good at many things, but was especially talented and skilled at...

_____

_____

_____

_____

"Anyone can be a father, but it takes someone special to be a dad." – Author Unknown

My dad and I are alike in these ways...

_____

_____

_____

_____

_____

_____

And this is how we are different...

_____

_____

_____

_____

_____

"Noble fathers have noble children."
– Euripides

I would describe our relationship when I was a kid this way...

_____

_____

_____

_____

...and this way during my teens...

_____

_____

_____

_____

...and in my later years...

_____

_____

_____

_____

"People who think they know everything are a great annoyance to those of us who do."
— Isaac Asimov

One of my favorite memories of my father is...

_____

_____

_____

_____

_____

_____

_____

Some of the best advice he gave me was...

_____

_____

_____

_____

_____

"The problem with parenting is that by the time you are experienced, you are unemployed."
– Author Unknown

The story of the way my parents met is...

_____

_____

_____

_____

_____

_____

_____

They were married on this date...

_____

Their ages when they were married were...

_____

_____

"The child supplies the power, but the parents have to do the steering." – Benjamin Spock

I would describe their relationship this way...

_____

_____

_____

_____

_____

_____

Their relationship influenced and impacted how I feel about love, relationships, and marriage in the following ways...

_____

_____

_____

_____

_____

_____

"A child cannot have too many people who love them and want to help them succeed." – Author Unknown

A list of people other than my parents who helped raise me includes...

_____

_____

_____

_____

_____

_____

_____

_____

_____

_____

_____

"Grandparents are a little bit parent, a little bit teacher, and a little bit best friend."

– Author Unknown

"Grandparents are both our past and our future. In some ways they are what has gone before, and in others they are what we will become." – Fred Rogers

My grandparents' names on my mother's side are...

_____

_____

My maternal grandmother's maiden name was...

_____

I called them...

_____

This is when and where they were born and where they grew up...

_____

_____

Their highest level of schooling was...

_____

_____

Their occupations were...

_____

_____

_____

"Beautiful young people are accidents of nature, but beautiful old people are works of art."
– Marjory Barslow-Greenbie

I would describe my grandparents on my mother's side this way...

_____

_____

_____

_____

_____

_____

_____

_____

_____

_____

_____

_____

"Grandparents are there to help the child get into mischief they haven't thought of yet."
– Author Unknown

My grandparents' names on my father's side are...

_____

_____

My paternal grandmother's maiden name was...

_____

I called them...

_____

This is when and where they were born and where they grew up...

_____

_____

Their highest level of schooling was...

_____

_____

Their occupations were...

_____

_____

_____

"If nothing is going well, call your grandmother."
– Italian Proverb

I would describe my grandparents on my father's side this way...

_____

_____

_____

_____

_____

_____

_____

_____

_____

_____

_____

_____

"The simplest toy, one which even the youngest child can operate, is called a grandparent." – Sam Levinson

When I think about my maternal and paternal grandparents' homes, these are the memories that come to mind...

_____

_____

_____

_____

_____

_____

_____

_____

_____

_____

_____

"Sibling: a combination of a best friend and a pain in the neck."
– Author Unknown

"Siblings: your only enemy you can't live without."
– Author Unknown

I have this many brothers and sisters...

_____

I was the oldest/middle/youngest or only child...

_____

My siblings' names and birthdates are...

_____

_____

_____

_____

_____

_____

_____

_____

"Siblings are a lens through which we can see what really happened in our childhoods." – Author Unknown

The sibling I was the closest to when I was growing up was...

_____

_____

And the sibling I am closest to now is...

_____

_____

The sibling I have the most in common with is...

_____

_____

Of all of us, the most athletic is...

_____

_____

And this is the smartest...

_____

_____

And the one who is the most family oriented is...

_____

_____

"What strange creatures brothers are!"
– Jane Austen

The last time we all got together was...

_____

_____

This is how I would describe that gathering and who was there...

_____

_____

_____

_____

_____

_____

_____

_____

_____

"Because of you, I will always have a friend."
– Author Unknown

A letter to my siblings...

_____

_____

_____

_____

_____

_____

_____

_____

_____

_____

_____

"Brothers and sisters are as close as hands and feet."
– Vietnamese Proverb

A letter to my siblings...

_____

_____

_____

_____

_____

_____

_____

_____

_____

_____

_____

"Not always eye to eye, but always heart to heart."
– Author Unknown

A letter to my siblings...

_____

_____

_____

_____

_____

_____

_____

_____

_____

_____

_____

"If life was a cookie, our siblings would be the chocolate chips." – Author Unknown

A letter to my siblings...

_____

_____

_____

_____

_____

_____

_____

_____

_____

_____

_____

"Love doesn't make the world go 'round. Love is what makes the ride worthwhile." – Franklin P. Jones

"Love is composed of a single soul inhabiting two bodies." – Aristotle

I believe...

- ☐ In soul mates.
- ☐ In love at first sight.
- ☐ That love can last forever.
- ☐ In long-distance relationships.
- ☐ That you can be friends with an ex.
- ☐ In marriage.
- ☐ In divorce.
- ☐ It is important to celebrate Valentine's Day.
- ☐ In summer flings/vacation romances.
- ☐ In second chances.
- ☐ In third chances.
- ☐ It is okay to kiss on the first date.
- ☐ In romantic surprises.
- ☐ One can find love through online dating.
- ☐ A relationship can survive infidelity.
- ☐ It is perfectly okay to live together without being married.
- ☐ Loving yourself should come before loving someone else.
- ☐ It is okay to prioritize personal goals over your relationship.
- ☐ That it is okay to move to be with someone.
- ☐ Couples should know the details of each other's past relationships.
- ☐ It is better to be single than to be in an unstimulating and humdrum relationship.

"Love is friendship set to music."
– Jackson Pollock

First loves...

I had my first kiss when I was _____ years old.

It was with....

_____

I had my first date when I was _____ years old.

It was with...

_____

We did the following on that date...

_____

_____

_____

I was _____ years old when I had my first serious long-term relationship.

It was with...

_____

It ended because...

_____

_____

_____

"Whatever our souls are made of, his and mine are the same." – Emily Brontë, *Wuthering Heights*

To me, the most important factor in keeping a relationship strong and healthy is...

_____

_____

_____

The couple I think is a model for a great relationship is...

_____

_____

The qualities I admire the most about their relationship are...

_____

_____

_____

_____

My top three relationship deal breakers are...

1. _____

2. _____

3. _____

"I love her, and that's the beginning and end of everything." – F. Scott Fitzgerald

This is how I know I have fallen in love...

_____

_____

_____

_____

_____

_____

And this is how I know if I have fallen out of love...

_____

_____

_____

_____

_____

_____

"The best thing to hold onto in life is each other."
– Audrey Hepburn

Over the course of my life, I have been in love this many times...

_____

And I have had this many serious long-term relationships...

_____

I have been married or had a partner this many times...

_____

_____

The story of meeting my current partner/spouse is...

_____

_____

_____

_____

_____

_____

_____

"To the world you may be one person, but to one person you are the world." – Author Unknown

The story of how I proposed/was proposed to is...

_____

_____

_____

_____

_____

_____

_____

_____

This is the date we were married...

_____

_____

"To love oneself is the beginning of a lifelong romance." – Oscar Wilde

This is what our wedding was like...

_____

_____

_____

_____

_____

_____

_____

And this is what we did for our honeymoon...

_____

_____

_____

_____

"If you can't take a joke, don't become a parent."
– Author Unknown

"Making the decision to have a child is momentous. It is to decide forever to have your heart go walking around outside your body." – Elizabeth Stone

I was this age when I first decided that one day, I wanted to have kids...

_____

_____

And I was this age when I first became a parent...

_____

Our kids were planned/surprises...

_____

_____

_____

My child's/children's names and dates of birth/adoption are...

_____

_____

_____

_____

_____

"Setting a good example for your children takes all the fun out of middle age." – William Feather

The stories of each of their births/adoptions are...

_____

_____

_____

_____

_____

_____

_____

_____

_____

_____

"We never know the love of a parent till we become parents ourselves." – Henry Ward Beecher

The stories of each of their births/adoptions are...

_____

_____

_____

_____

_____

_____

_____

_____

_____

_____

_____

"If you want your children to listen, try talking softly to someone else." – Ann Landers

Their first words were...

_____

_____

_____

_____

_____

_____

And they were these ages when they took their first steps...

_____

_____

_____

_____

_____

_____

"A child fills a place in your heart that you never knew was empty." – Author Unknown

When they were little, I remember reading these books to them...

_____

_____

_____

_____

_____

And singing these songs...

_____

_____

_____

_____

_____

When they were upset, I would calm them by...

_____

_____

_____

"The moments we share are the moments we keep forever." – Author Unknown

The stories of each of my kid's childhood and teenage years are...

_____

_____

_____

_____

_____

_____

_____

_____

_____

_____

_____

"Everything depends on upbringing."
– Leo Tolstoy, *War and Peace*

The stories of each of my kid's childhood and teenage years are...

_____

_____

_____

_____

_____

_____

_____

_____

_____

_____

"My father gave me the greatest gift anyone could give another person; he believed in me." – Jim Valvano

The stories of each of my kid's childhood and teenage years are...

_____

_____

_____

_____

_____

_____

_____

_____

_____

_____

_____

"Don't worry that children never listen to you; worry that they are always watching you." – Robert Fulghum

The stories of each of my kid's childhood and teenage years are...

_____

_____

_____

_____

_____

_____

_____

_____

_____

_____

_____

"It is easier to build strong children than to repair broken men." – Frederick Douglass

The stories of each of my kid's adult years are...

_____

_____

_____

_____

_____

_____

_____

_____

_____

_____

"What a difference it makes to come home to a child!" –
Margaret Fuller

The stories of each of my kid's adult years are...

_____

_____

_____

_____

_____

_____

_____

_____

_____

_____

_____

"Children are likely to live up to what you believe of them." – Lady Bird Johnson

The stories of each of my kid's adult years are...

_____

_____

_____

_____

_____

_____

_____

_____

_____

_____

"The soul is healed by being with children."
– Fyodor Dostoevsky

The stories of each of my kid's adult years are...

_____

_____

_____

_____

_____

_____

_____

_____

_____

_____

_____

"Be the parent you want them to remember."
– Author Unknown

In my opinion, the biggest differences in how kids are raised today and when I was young are...

_____

_____

_____

_____

_____

_____

_____

_____

_____

_____

_____

"Tell me and I forget, teach me and I may remember, involve me and I learn." – Benjamin Franklin

Looking back, the biggest changes I would make in how I raised my kids are...

_____

_____

_____

_____

_____

_____

_____

_____

_____

_____

"No matter the amount of time or distance, we are a part of our parents and they us." – Author Unknown

The best parts of being a parent are...

_____

_____

_____

_____

_____

_____

_____

_____

_____

_____

_____

_____

"Adults are just outdated children."
– Theodore Giesel

And the hardest parts of being a parent are...

_____

_____

_____

_____

_____

_____

_____

_____

_____

_____

_____

"I think one of life's great milestones is when a person can look back and be almost as thankful for the setbacks as for the victories."

– Bob Dole

Our lives are directed by a handful of decisions and events that recast everything.

Milestone Moments

When we look at our own life course, we see times when our path has been smooth and unheeded and other stretches when it has been winding and uphill with stops and starts along the way.

We discover instances when our life path suddenly became harder – or easier – or went in a completely different direction.

These are those milestone moments, marks of time when we made a key decision, when something transformative happened to us, or when a goal we were working for was finally achieved.

Keeping these milestone moments fresh in our minds allows us to learn, to grow, to give thanks, and to celebrate. This awareness makes us stronger, and more understanding that one single day can change everything.

Remembering and knowing that a single choice or a single day can change everything helps us cherish each and every day that makes up our life. We become more willing to make hard choices and take positive risks.

We become brave in our goals, and we work harder to achieve them. We see more of our self-value, and we make ourselves and our ambitions a priority.

"When people throw stones at you, convert them into milestones." – Author Unknown

A milestone moment I can identify in my life is...

_____

_____

_____

The conditions and circumstances that led up to this moment were...

_____

_____

_____

This milestone moment resulted in these changes to me and my life...

_____

_____

_____

_____

_____

"Remember to celebrate milestones as you prepare for the road ahead." – Nelson Mandela

Studying what led up to and what resulted from this milestone moment has taught me and helped me understand the following...

_____

_____

_____

_____

_____

_____

_____

_____

_____

_____

_____

"A milestone is less date and more definition."
– Rands

A second milestone moment I can identify is...

_____

_____

_____

The conditions and circumstances that led up to this moment were...

_____

_____

_____

_____

This milestone moment resulted in these changes to me and my life...

_____

_____

_____

_____

"Choices are the hinges of destiny."
– Edwin Markham

Studying what led up to and what resulted from this milestone moment has taught me and helped me understand the following...

_____

_____

_____

_____

_____

_____

_____

_____

_____

_____

_____

_____

_____

"Sometimes the hardest thing and the right thing are the same thing." – Author Unknown

A third milestone moment I can identify is...

_____

_____

_____

The conditions and circumstances that led up to this moment were...

_____

_____

_____

This milestone moment resulted in these changes to me and my life...

_____

_____

_____

_____

_____

"Indecision is a decision."
– Author Unknown

Studying what led up to and what resulted from this milestone moment
has taught me and helped me understand the following...

_____

_____

_____

_____

_____

_____

_____

_____

_____

_____

"One cannot think well, love well, sleep well, if one has not dined well."
– Virginia Woolf,
A Room of One's Own

"First we eat, then we do everything else."
– M.F.K. Fisher

A food item that reminds me of my childhood is...

_____

_____

Specifically, when I think of this dish, I remember...

_____

_____

_____

_____

My personal food and dietary related preferences are...

_____

_____

_____

_____

_____

"My weaknesses have always been food and men – in that order." – Dolly Parton

My cooking skills are...

- ☐ Let's order out.

- ☐ I won't make anyone sick.

- ☐ I have a few things that I cook well.

- ☐ I am ready for my own cookbook, cooking show, and restaurant!

The first thing I learned to cook was...

_____

_____

The family recipe I want to learn to cook is...

_____

_____

_____

If I could have dinner with any five people who have ever lived, I would invite...

_____

_____

_____

_____

"Life itself is the proper binge."
– Julia Child

This is what I would order for my last meal...

_____

_____

_____

_____

_____

_____

_____

_____

_____

_____

_____

"Let food be thy medicine and medicine be thy food."
– Hippocrates

My favorite thing to eat is...

_____

_____

_____

I like my eggs cooked this way...

_____

_____

And my steak cooked this way...

_____

_____

My favorite pizza toppings are...

_____

_____

My thoughts on pineapple as a pizza topping are...

_____

Sweet or salty? _____

Cake or pie? _____

"Life is uncertain. Eat dessert first."
– Ernestine Ulmer

My favorite dessert is...

_____

_____

My favorite flavor of ice cream is...

_____

_____

My opinion of having breakfast for dinner is...

_____

_____

_____

When I was a kid, my mother would make me this when I wasn't feeling well...

_____

_____

_____

My favorite beverage is...

_____

_____

"To eat is a necessity, but to eat intelligently is an art."
– François de la Rochefoucauld

Beer or wine? _____

My go-to cocktail is...

_____

_____

_____

My typical coffee shop order is...

_____

_____

_____

My top three favorite restaurants are...

_____

_____

_____

My go-to fast-food restaurant is...

_____

_____

"Laughter is brightest where food is best."
– Irish Proverb

Favorite fruit: _____

Favorite vegetable: _____

My taste and tolerance for spicy food is...

_____

_____

_____

My favorite food cuisines are...

_____

_____

_____

_____

The most adventurous food I have ever eaten is...

_____

_____

_____

_____

"Be who you are and say what you feel, because those who mind don't matter, and those who matter don't mind." – Bernard M. Maruch

"Always be a first-rate version of yourself and not a second-rate version of someone else." – Judy Garland

My favorite color is...

_____

My first pet was...

_____

_____

My favorite season of the year is...

_____

My first trip out of the country was to...

_____

_____

_____

My favorite holiday is...

_____

_____

My go-to karaoke song is...

_____

_____

"Failure is the condiment that gives success its flavor." – Truman Capote

My biggest fear is...

_____

_____

_____

The superpower I would pick for myself is...

_____

_____

The first ocean I ever saw was...

_____

_____

The first time I ever saw snow was...

_____

_____

_____

My favorite guilty pleasure is...

_____

_____

"If you do what you love, you'll never work a day in your life." – Marc Anthony

The celebrity I am most often told I look like is...

_____

_____

I celebrated my 16th birthday by...

_____

_____

_____

I celebrated my 21st birthday by...

_____

_____

_____

The first time I truly felt like an adult was...

_____

_____

_____

_____

"The time is always right to do what is right."
— Martin Luther King Jr.

If I could live anywhere in the world for a year with all expenses paid, I would choose to live here...

_____

_____

My morning routine is...

_____

_____

_____

_____

So far, the ten-year period of my life that I most fondly look back on is...

_____

_____

_____

I think I remember this time so warmly because...

_____

_____

_____

"I think one day you'll find that you're the hero you've been looking for." – Jimmy Stewart

My first best friend was...

_____

_____

My longest friendship has been with...

_____

_____

I have known them since...

_____

_____

The story of how we met is...

_____

_____

_____

_____

_____

_____

"We lose ourselves in things we love. We find ourselves there, too." – Kristin Martz

My favorite sports teams are...

_____

_____

_____

_____

_____

My favorite sports memory is...

_____

_____

_____

_____

_____

"The privilege of a lifetime is to become who you truly are." – Carl Jung

My favorite travel memory is...

_____

_____

_____

_____

_____

_____

_____

_____

_____

_____

"For every minute you are angry you lose sixty seconds of happiness." – Ralph Waldo Emerson

I identify myself politically as...

_____

The first election I voted in was...

_____

The main ways my political views have changed over the course of my life are...

_____

_____

_____

_____

If I woke up tomorrow to find myself in charge of the country, the first three things I would enact or change are...

1. _____

_____

2. _____

_____

3. _____

_____

"You can't cross the sea merely by standing and staring at the water." – Rabindranath Tagore

A few of my favorite places I have traveled to are...

_____

_____

_____

_____

_____

_____

_____

_____

_____

_____

_____

"I am not what happened to me, I am what I choose to become." — Carl Jung

The religious and spiritual practices that are a part of my daily life are...

_____

_____

_____

_____

_____

The ways my spiritual and religious practices have changed and evolved over the course of my life are...

_____

_____

_____

_____

_____

"Life isn't about finding yourself. Life is about creating yourself." — George Bernard Shaw

If I had to choose between fate or free will, I believe this one has the biggest impact on our lives:

_____

A miracle I have personally experienced is...

_____

_____

_____

_____

_____

When times are tough, this is how I give myself the inner-strength I need...

_____

_____

_____

_____

_____

"We can complain because rose bushes have thorns, or rejoice because thorns have roses."
– Alphonse Karr,
A Tour Round My Garden

"If the only prayer you said was thank you, that would be enough." – Meister Eckhart

Our lives are full of commonplace things that we take for granted. Paying attention to and being grateful for these things can help us manage some of the stress and hardships of life.

My list of everyday things I am grateful for includes...

_____

_____

_____

_____

_____

_____

_____

_____

_____

_____

"If you are going through Hell, keep going."
– Winston Churchill

Challenges and failures are frustrating parts of life. While they can sometimes sap our hopes and weaken our disposition, they can also provide the motivation and provocation needed to make key life changes and decisions.

Looking back, a few of the things that created hardship and feelings of dejection for me, but later led to positive transformations in my life, are...

_____

_____

_____

_____

_____

_____

_____

_____

_____

"Gratitude is not only the greatest of virtues, but the parent of all others." – Marcus Tullius Cicero

I am grateful for...

These photos:

_____

_____

_____

_____

These friends:

_____

_____

_____

_____

These teachers/professors/mentors:

_____

_____

_____

"Piglet noticed that even though he had a very small heart, it could hold a rather large amount of gratitude." – A.A. Milne, *Winnie-the-Pooh*

I am grateful for...

This risk I took:

_____

_____

_____

_____

This sacrifice I made:

_____

_____

_____

_____

This gift I recently received:

_____

_____

_____

_____

"I awoke excited, remembering this is the first and last time I will get to experience and learn from this day." – Author Unknown

I am grateful for...

This thing about myself:

_____

_____

_____

_____

_____

This big change I made in my life:

_____

_____

_____

_____

_____

"Gratitude turns what we have into enough."
– Author Unknown

I am grateful for...

This hard decision I made:

_____

_____

_____

_____

_____

This thing I do every day:

_____

_____

_____

_____

_____

"Gratitude is riches. Complaining is poverty."
– Doris Day

I am grateful for...

This talent or skill I have:

_____

_____

_____

_____

This part of my job:

_____

_____

_____

_____

This thing I recently purchased:

_____

_____

_____

_____

"There are only two ways to live your life. One is as though nothing is a miracle. The other is as though everything is a miracle." – Albert Einstein

I am grateful for...

This thing that happened today:

_____

_____

_____

_____

_____

This thing I recently learned:

_____

_____

_____

_____

_____

"When I started counting my blessings, my whole life turned around." – Willie Nelson

I am grateful for...

This piece of advice I was given:

_____

_____

_____

_____

_____

This thing that I really wanted to happen but didn't:

_____

_____

_____

_____

_____

"Life is a journey with problems to solve, lessons to learn, but most of all, experiences to enjoy."
– Author Unknown

"Life is a great big canvas, and you should throw all the paint on it you can." – Danny Kaye

I have...

☐ Traveled overseas.

☐ Flown in a plane.

☐ Had surgery.

☐ Milked a cow.

☐ Been in a fist fight.

☐ Gone on a blind date.

☐ Had my tonsils removed.

☐ Made a speech in front of a large group.

☐ Sung a solo in front of an audience.

☐ Been arrested.

☐ Ridden a motorcycle.

☐ Shot a gun.

☐ Ridden in a hot air balloon.

☐ Gone on a cruise.

☐ Lied to a police officer.

☐ Gone scuba diving.

☐ Had stiches.

☐ Run a marathon.

☐ Agreed to be someone else's alibi.

☐ Gone bungee jumping.

☐ Skipped school.

"The only true wisdom is in knowing you know nothing." – Socrates

I have...

- ☐ Lost a significant amount of weight.
- ☐ Ridden in a helicopter.
- ☐ Gotten a tattoo.
- ☐ Been to a Broadway musical.
- ☐ Used a fake ID.
- ☐ Been to a professional sporting event.
- ☐ Met a celebrity.
- ☐ Gone skydiving.
- ☐ Broken a bone.
- ☐ Cheated on a test.
- ☐ Been to a large music festival.
- ☐ Been robbed.
- ☐ Snooped through someone's medicine cabinet.
- ☐ Gone surfing.
- ☐ Performed in a play, musical, or opera.
- ☐ Gone on a multi-day road trip.
- ☐ Lied to get out of work.
- ☐ Gone backpacking.
- ☐ Snuck into a movie.
- ☐ Stood up a date.
- ☐ Been stood up.

"And in the end, it's not the years in your life that count. It's the life in your years." – Abraham Lincoln

I have...

- ☐ Gotten a speeding ticket.
- ☐ Gotten out of a speeding ticket.
- ☐ Crashed a party.
- ☐ Had a crush on a teacher or boss.
- ☐ Been selected for a jury.
- ☐ Given someone a fake name or phone number.
- ☐ Been in a band.
- ☐ Had a near death experience.
- ☐ Performed CPR or the Heimlich Maneuver on someone.
- ☐ Driven in a country where they drive on the other side of the road.
- ☐ Driven a jet ski?
- ☐ Driven a snowmobile?
- ☐ Played spin the bottle.
- ☐ Built a sandcastle.
- ☐ Seen a meteor shower.
- ☐ Crowd-surfed at a music concert.
- ☐ Seen a ghost.
- ☐ Learned a second language.
- ☐ Been stuck in an elevator.
- ☐ Gone hunting.
- ☐ Had my palm read.

"Fill your life with experiences. Not things. Have stories to tell, not stuff to show." – Author Unknown

I have...

- ☐ Broken off an engagement.

- ☐ Had braces.

- ☐ Traveled to Greece.

- ☐ Gone ice skating.

- ☐ Gone snow skiing.

- ☐ Been to a tropical island.

- ☐ Ridden in a train.

- ☐ Grown a vegetable garden.

- ☐ Started a business.

- ☐ Experienced an earthquake.

- ☐ Been in a hurricane.

- ☐ Donated blood.

- ☐ Made a snow angel.

- ☐ Been where a tornado struck down.

- ☐ Lived in a foreign country.

- ☐ Slept outside under the stars.

- ☐ Been to a hot spring.

- ☐ Gone sailing.

- ☐ Been to a rodeo.

- ☐ Gone deep sea fishing.

- ☐ Ridden in a horse-drawn carriage.

"There are some things you have to experience to understand." – Oscar Wilde

I have...

- ☐ Texted something embarrassing or incriminating to the wrong person.

- ☐ Driven a tractor.

- ☐ Been in the middle of a mosh pit.

- ☐ Been to a topless/nude beach.

- ☐ Ridden a horse.

- ☐ Ridden a mechanical bull.

- ☐ Been a passenger in a private jet.

- ☐ Dyed my hair.

- ☐ Had my picture taken with someone famous.

- ☐ Ridden in a gondola in Venice.

- ☐ Been a maid of honor/best man.

- ☐ Re-gifted a gift.

- ☐ Been on television.

- ☐ Seen a UFO.

- ☐ Gone skinny-dipping.

- ☐ Been knocked unconscious.

- ☐ Participated in a political protest.

- ☐ Attended the ballet.

- ☐ Fixed someone up (romantically).

- ☐ Attended the opera.

"Forgiveness isn't about changing the past; it is all about changing the future." – Author Unknown

"Forgiveness is choosing to love. It is the first skill of self-giving love." – Mahatma Gandhi

My personal definition of forgiveness is...

_____

_____

_____

_____

_____

_____

Forgiveness is important because...

_____

_____

_____

_____

_____

_____

"Hating someone makes them important. Forgiving makes them obsolete." – Author Unknown

A person from my life who I have bad feelings about because of something they did in the past is...

_____

_____

_____

When I think about what happened with this person, my emotional response is...

_____

_____

_____

_____

_____

_____

_____

_____

"Genuine forgiveness does not deny anger but faces it head-on." – Alice Duer Miller

I am allowing myself to carry these negative feelings because...

_____

_____

_____

_____

_____

Continuing to hold these feelings about what happened impacts me and my life this way...

_____

_____

_____

_____

_____

"Forgiveness is a virtue of the brave."
– Indira Gandhi

The things that are preventing me from forgiving this person and moving forward are...

_____

_____

_____

_____

_____

_____

When I think about it, this is what I think forgiving this person would do for me...

_____

_____

_____

_____

_____

"Forgiveness does not change the past, but it does enlarge the future." – Author Unknown

One way to move forward, no longer letting this be a part of me, is to...

_____

_____

_____

_____

_____

_____

_____

_____

_____

_____

"Why should they forgive you when you won't forgive yourself?" – Author Unknown

A regret from the past that weighs on me is...

_____

_____

_____

_____

_____

Continuing to carry around this self-blame and regret is impairing me in these ways...

_____

_____

_____

_____

_____

_____

"What is unforgiven from yesterday will define who and how we are tomorrow." – Author Unknown

Moving forward and no longer carrying this regret would...

_____

_____

_____

_____

_____

One way I could release myself of this regret and move forward is...

_____

_____

_____

_____

_____

_____

_____

"Every child is an artist. The problem is how to remain an artist once we grow up." – Pablo Picasso

"Music is love in search of a word."
– Collette

In my opinion, the best decades for music are...

_____

_____

_____

_____

And the best genres of music are...

_____

_____

_____

_____

The first album/tape/cd I can remember buying was...

_____

_____

_____

"Music expresses that which cannot be put into words and that which cannot remain silent." – Victor Hugo

The first concert I attended was...

_____

_____

A few of my favorite musicians and bands of all time are...

_____

_____

_____

_____

Over the course of my life, my taste in music has changed in this way...

_____

_____

_____

_____

"Everything I learned I learned from the movies."
– Audrey Hepburn

If I could pick to see a live show by any musician/band who has ever existed, I would choose...

_____

The movie I have watched the greatest number of times is...

_____

_____

The movies that have had the biggest impacts on me are...

_____

_____

_____

_____

A few of my favorite actors and actresses are...

_____

_____

_____

_____

"Television is an invention that permits you to be entertained in your living room by people you wouldn't have in your home." – David Frost

The television shows (sports, news, series, specials, etc.) that left the biggest impression on me are...

_____

_____

_____

_____

_____

In my opinion, the best movie or television version of a book I have read is...

_____

_____

A few of my favorite authors are...

_____

_____

_____

_____

"How long is forever? Sometimes just one second."
— Lewis Carroll, *Alice's Adventures in Wonderland*

The books that have majorly impacted the way I think, work, or live my life are...

1. _____

2. _____

3. _____

4. _____

5. _____

6. _____

7. _____

8. _____

9. _____

10. _____

11. _____

12. _____

13. _____

14. _____

15. _____

"Television is chewing gum for the eyes."
— Frank Lloyd Wright

My top ten favorite television shows of all time...

1. _____

2. _____

3. _____

4. _____

5. _____

6. _____

7. _____

8. _____

9. _____

10. _____

"Every great film should seem new each time you see it." – Roger Ebert

My top ten favorite movies of all time...

1. _____

2. _____

3. _____

4. _____

5. _____

6. _____

7. _____

8. _____

9. _____

10. _____

"Where words fail, music speaks."
– Hans Christian Andersen

If I were to create a playlist of my favorite music throughout my life, it would include these songs and musical compositions:

1. _____

2. _____

3. _____

4. _____

5. _____

6. _____

7. _____

8. _____

9. _____

10. _____

11. _____

12. _____

13. _____

14. _____

15. _____

"Without music, life would be a blank to me."
– Jane Austen, *Emma*

1. _____

2. _____

3. _____

4. _____

5. _____

6. _____

7. _____

8. _____

9. _____

10. _____

11. _____

12. _____

13. _____

14. _____

15. _____

"Somebody should tell us, right at the start of our lives, that we are dying. Then we might live life to the limit, every minute of every day."
– Pope Paul VI

"Don't be afraid your life will end; be afraid that it will never begin." – Author Unknown

Fifteen things I want to do before I leave this life...

1. _____

2. _____

3. _____

4. _____

5. _____

6. _____

7. _____

8. _____

9. _____

10. _____

11. _____

12. _____

13. _____

14. _____

15. _____

"There will be two dates on your tombstone and all that's gonna matter is that little dash between 'em." – Kevin Welch

Fifteen things I want to learn before I leave this life...

1. _____

2. _____

3. _____

4. _____

5. _____

6. _____

7. _____

8. _____

9. _____

10. _____

11. _____

12. _____

13. _____

14. _____

15. _____

"The saddest summary of a life contains three descriptions: could have, might have, and should have." – Louis E. Boone

Fifteen places I want to travel to before I leave this life...

1. _____

2. _____

3. _____

4. _____

5. _____

6. _____

7. _____

8. _____

9. _____

10. _____

11. _____

12. _____

13. _____

14. _____

15. _____

"Endings are just beginnings in disguise."
– Author Unknown

I believe that this is what happens to us after this life ends...

_____

_____

_____

_____

_____

_____

_____

_____

_____

_____

_____

"Cherish your yesterdays, dream your tomorrows and live your todays." – Author Unknown

This is how I hope I will be remembered after I have moved on...

_____

_____

_____

_____

_____

_____

_____

_____

_____

_____

_____

"When you cease to dream you cease to live."
– Malcolm Forbes

In case of my death, this is my Letter of Wishes...

I would like to be (buried, cremated, or something else):

_____

_____

Make my arrangements with this funeral home:

_____

_____

My preference is for the following to be held:

☐ Funeral

☐ Memorial service

☐ Other: _____

_____

_____

_____

_____

_____

_____

"In order to write about life first you must live it."
— Ernest Hemingway

My wishes, in detail, for how my life and relationships will be celebrated are...

_____

_____

_____

_____

_____

_____

_____

_____

_____

_____

_____

"Every moment is a fresh beginning."
– T.S. Eliot

The obituary or eulogy that I would write for myself would go something like this...

_____

_____

_____

_____

_____

_____

_____

_____

_____

_____

"To die will be an awfully big adventure."
– J.M. Barrie

_____

_____

_____

_____

_____

_____

_____

_____

_____

_____

_____

"The purpose of life is not to be happy. It is to be useful, to be honorable, to be compassionate, to have it make some difference that you have lived and lived well." – Ralph Waldo Emerson

"Not until we are lost do we begin to understand ourselves." – Henry David Thoreau

A letter to my teenage self...

_____

_____

_____

_____

_____

_____

_____

_____

_____

_____

_____

_____

"Sometimes when things are falling apart, they may actually be falling into place." – Author Unknown

A letter to myself when I was in the middle of my hardest life moment...

_____

_____

_____

_____

_____

_____

_____

_____

_____

_____

_____

_____

"Whatever you want to do, do it now! There are only so many tomorrows." – Michael Landon

A letter to myself five years from now...

_____

_____

_____

_____

_____

_____

_____

_____

_____

_____

_____

"It takes a deep commitment to change and an even deeper commitment to grow." — Ralph Ellison

Write a personal note to a specific person in your life:

A letter to...

"I've got a great ambition to die of exhaustion rather than boredom." – Thomas Carlyle

A letter to...

_____

_____

_____

_____

_____

_____

_____

_____

_____

_____

"The best and most beautiful things in the world cannot be seen or even touched – they must be felt with the heart." – Helen Keller

The following pages are for you to expand on some of your answers, to share more memories, and/or to write notes to your loved ones:

A letter to...

_____

_____

_____

_____

_____

_____

_____

_____

_____

_____

"Don't judge each day by the harvest that you reap but by the seeds that you plant."
– Robert Louis Stevenson

A letter to...

_____

_____

_____

_____

_____

_____

_____

_____

_____

_____

_____

"Each person must live their life as a model for others." – Rosa Parks

_____

_____

_____

_____

_____

_____

_____

_____

_____

_____

_____

"In three words I can sum up everything I've learned about life: it goes on." – Robert Frost

_____

_____

_____

_____

_____

_____

_____

_____

_____

_____

_____

_____

_____

"Believe you can and you're halfway there."
– Theodore Roosevelt

"Life is not a matter of holding good cards, but sometimes, playing a poor hand well." – Jack London

_____

_____

_____

_____

_____

_____

_____

_____

_____

_____

_____

Hear Your Story Books

At **Hear Your Story**, we have created a line of books focused on giving each of us a place to tell the unique story of who we are, where we have been, and where we are going.

Sharing and hearing the stories of the people in our lives creates a closeness and understanding, ultimately strengthening our bonds.

Available at Amazon, all bookstores, and HearYourStoryBooks.com

Mom, I Want to Hear Your Story
A Mother's Guided Journal to Share Her Life & Her Love

Dad, I Want to Hear Your Story
A Father's Guided Journal to Share His Life & His Love

Grandmother, I Want to Hear Your Story
A Grandfather's Guided Journal to Share His Life and His Love

Grandfather, I Want to Hear Your Story
A Grandfather's Guided Journal to Share His Life and His Love

Tell Your Life Story
The Write Your Own Autobiography Guided Journal

Life Gave Me You; I Want to Hear Your Story
A Guided Journal for Stepmothers to Share Their Life Story

You Chose to Be My Dad; I Want to Hear Your Story
A Guided Journal for Stepdads to Share Their Life Story

To My Wonderful Aunt, I Want to Hear Your Story
A Guided Journal to Share Her Life and Her Love

Hear Your Story Books

To My Uncle, I Want to Hear Your Story
A Guided Journal to Share His Life and His Love

Mom, I Want to Learn Your Recipes
A Keepsake Memory Book to Gather and
Preserve Your Favorite Family Recipes

Dad, I Want to Learn Your Recipes
A Keepsake Memory Book to Gather and
Preserve Your Favorite Family Recipes

Grandmother, I Want to Learn Your Recipes
A Keepsake Memory Book to Gather and
Preserve Your Favorite Family Recipes

Grandfather, I Want to Learn Your Recipes
A Keepsake Memory Book to Gather and
Preserve Your Favorite Family Recipes

Aunt, I Want to Learn Your Recipes
A Keepsake Memory Book to Gather and
Preserve Your Favorite Family Recipes

Uncle, I Want to Learn Your Recipes
A Keepsake Memory Book to Gather and
Preserve Your Favorite Family Recipes

To My Girlfriend, I Want to Hear Your Story

To My Boyfriend, I Want to Hear Your Story

Mom & Me: Let's Learn Together Journal for Kids

About Hear Your Story

The adventures we go on, the people we love, the moments that shape us - our experiences link together like chapters in a book to form our unique and never-to-be-repeated story.

At **Hear Your Story**, our mission is to create a place and a way for anyone to easily share and preserve their life story. We passionately believe that within everyone is a treasure of memories and stories that need to be told, cherished, and passed on through generations.

The beginnings of **Hear Your Story** are from a deeply personal space.

After seeing the cruelness of Alzheimer's steal his father's creativity, curiosity, and memories, our founder struggled with feelings of helplessness and regret. From his grief came the mission at the heart of **Hear Your Story** – to create a simple and elegant way for memories to be shared and protected.

We are devoted to helping anyone tell their story, in their words, and create their legacy. No one's memories should be lost to time when there is so much meaning, joy, and love to be shared in remembering.

Hear Your Story family memory journals are lovingly crafted with thoughtfulness and skill. With each carefully chosen question, we gently guide you or your loved one down memory lane, making it simple and fun to reminisce, chronicle, and pass on life's tales.

Gifting a **Hear Your Story** journal to a loved one or yourself is more than just presenting a beautifully crafted journal; it's gifting the joy of reminiscence, the power of reflection, and the understanding that comes with connection.

As our journals find their way to nightstands and coffee tables, we envision families coming together, children nestled close, listening, learning, and realizing the depth and connection of their roots.

So, come, let's journey and learn together. Because every memory is a story waiting to be heard.

And **Hear Your Story** is here to ensure it is told.

ISBN: 978-1-955034-15-9

Made in United States
Troutdale, OR
12/10/2023

15595231R00117